► ROSEMARY FEASEY ◄

SCIENCE
in action
5 to 16

Key Stage 2 – Teacher's Guide

LHBEC

Nelson Blackie

Thomas Nelson and Sons Ltd
Nelson House Mayfield Road
Walton-on-Thames Surrey
KT12 5PL UK

51 York Place
Edinburgh
EH1 3JD UK

Nelson Blackie
Wester Cleddens Road
Bishopbriggs
Glasgow
G64 2NZ UK

Thomas Nelson (Hong Kong) Ltd
Toppan Building 10/F
22A Westlands Road
Quarry Bay Hong Kong

Thomas Nelson Australia
102 Dodds Street
South Melbourne
Victoria 3205 Australia

Nelson Canada
1120 Birchmount Road
Scarborough Ontario
M1K 5G4 Canada

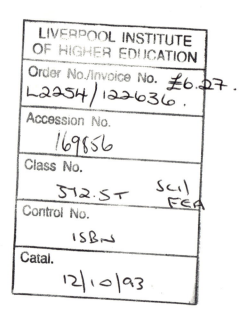

First published by Thomas Nelson and Sons Ltd 1993

ISBN 0-17-423303-5
NPN 9 8 7 6 5 4 3 2 1

Printed in Great Britain by
Hobbs the Printers Ltd, Southampton, S09 2UZ

CONTENTS

INTRODUCTION

Science in Action - 5 to 16 offers a flexible approach to the teaching of science through a wide range of activities set in everyday contexts which are relevant to children. The activities develop the skills and strategies vital to the 'doing' of science and continually refine knowledge and understanding. Of particular emphasis throughout the scheme is the development of the pupil's ability to handle investigations as these play such a prominent part in Science in the National Curriculum.

The course is based on the programmes of study for science and provides full coverage of the revised attainment targets. Pupils are given the opportunity to revisit statements of attainment throughout the course, allowing reinforcement of skills, knowledge and understanding. Once ideas and methods of working have been introduced they are developed in subsequent Key Stages. This enables a pyramid or cluster group of schools to provide a progressive science course for children from the time they enter school until they leave at 16.

Science in Action - 5 to 16 encourages children to take decisions about their own learning and helps to place the teacher in a supportive role. The development of collaborative methods of working is another key feature of the course. Children are challenged to ask questions and then seek their own answers through cooperation with other children and adults.

The Key Stage 2 Science in Action - 5 to 16 books have been designed to be of use in a wide range of school situations and with a variety of teaching and learning styles. The pupils' pages are photocopiable, and each is backed-up with an accompanying page of teacher's notes which includes:
- starting points to introduce the activity
- a background explanation of the knowledge and understanding covered
- advice on handling investigations and the variables involved
- safety aspects
- suggestions on how children could record their work.

Cross-curricular issues are fully acknowledged. Each unit has a cross-curricular topic web and every activity has a curriculum links section, which indicates how maths and language skills can be built into science classwork.

Assessment opportunities in science are indicated in tables in each Key Stage 2 book (1 to 4), and a photocopiable record sheet appears on page 27 of this book to assist the teacher with planning and recording assessment. This record sheet is designed to be transferable from one Key Stage to the next.

Activities are set in relevant everyday contexts.

AIMS OF SCIENCE IN ACTION - 5 TO 16 IN KEY STAGE 2

The books in this series set out to:

- Develop scientific concepts and an understanding of how to carry out investigations

- Encourage independent attitudes and ways of working

- Offer activities set in a range of interesting and relevant contexts accessible to all children

- Facilitate the transfer of skills into science from other areas of the curriculum

- Provide a comprehensive and balanced coverage for 7-11 year olds

- Provide support for the non-specialist teacher of science

- Introduce environmental issues and develop children's sense of responsibility towards the environment

- Develop children's understanding of the need to collect useful data

- Encourage children to be creative in finding their own solutions to problems and questions

- Develop children's ability to work independently or collaboratively within a group

- Encourage children to generate their own questions and ideas and to seek solutions

- Provide necessary reinforcement and development of skills and concepts

- Develop a wide range of methods of recording and communicating

- Give children a working understanding of safety issues

- Facilitate assessment as an integral part of pupils' work

THEMES IN SCIENCE IN ACTION - 5 TO 16 KEY STAGE 2

At Key Stage 2 **Science in Action - 5 to 16** consists of four photocopiable books and this teacher's guide.

Book 1 for Year 3 (8 year olds)
Book 2 for Year 4 (9 year olds)
Book 3 for Year 5 (10 year olds)
Book 4 for Year 6 (11 year olds)

Each book is based round the following themes which provide a range of starting points for work in science.

▶ SCIENCE FROM STORIES

The books used are:

The Lighthouse Keeper's Lunch (Book 1)
James and the Giant Peach (Book 2)
Dinosaurs and all that Rubbish (Book 3)
Swiss Family Robinson (Book 4)

The potential to link language and science is central to all the activities in these units.

▶ SCIENCE FROM THE WORLD OF WORK

Considering the world of work helps children to see the relevance of science to everyday life. Jobs covered include:
the baker
the builder
the clothes designer
the market gardener

▶ SCIENCE FROM LIVING THINGS

These units aim to develop the children's understanding of the diversity, complexity and interdependence of living things in the natural environment. The activities promote positive and responsible attitudes towards the environment.

▶ SCIENCE FROM HOME AND SCHOOL

Home and school environments offer opportunities for children to develop an understanding of a range of key concepts in activities directly relevant to their own lives.

▶ SCIENCE FROM MOVING AROUND

In these units children explore aspects of movement on land, air and in water. They also consider movement in space, and opportunities to use research skills to extend knowledge and understanding of the solar system are also included.

▶ SCIENCE FROM HAVING FUN

The activities in these units capitalise units on children's own interests and experiences by using a series of leisure contexts which include toys and fairgrounds. These contexts have high motivational value and ensure that science is fun.

Within each book, each theme contains nine activities and represents half a term's work.

THE WHOLE CURRICULUM IN SCIENCE IN ACTION - 5 to 16

Science in Action - 5 to 16 recognises that the place of science is within a broad and balanced curriculum for all pupils. The following indicates how issues related to the whole curriculum are addressed in a co-ordinated approach throughout the scheme.

CORE SUBJECTS

The core subjects of science, mathematics and English receive coverage throughout the Key Stage 1 and 2 materials.

Suggestions for work in maths and English can be found on the cross-curricular links pages and in the teacher's notes which accompany each activity. In the latter case they help indicate how aspects of science, maths and English can be developed within one activity and provide assessment opportunities.

FOUNDATION SUBJECTS

The foundation subjects plus R.E. are addressed in the cross-curricular links pages where appropriate to the context provided by each unit. Suggestions are given to assist the teacher in producing a topic which permeates the curriculum.

CROSS-CURRICULAR DIMENSIONS

Equal opportunities are central to **Science in Action - 5 to 16** which attempts to make science accessible to all children by placing science in contexts which are interesting, relevant and everyday.
Page 11 of this *Teacher's Guide* covers a range of issues associated with equal opportunities in science.

CROSS-CURRICULAR SKILLS

COMMUNICATION - **Science in Action - 5 to 16** suggests a range of methods to encourage children to communicate their science to a wide variety of audiences.
NUMERACY - Activities frequently demand the transfer and use of mathematical skills to a science context.
STUDY - Opportunities are offered to develop a range of study skills from researching information to planning work strategies.
PERSONAL AND SOCIAL - Pupils are encouraged to be independent decision makers who can work on their own or within a group situation with commitment, valuing the contribution of others.
INFORMATION TECHNOLOGY - The use of a wide range of information technology is suggested; from videos, and tape recorders to cameras, word processors and data logging programs.

CROSS-CURRICULAR THEMES

ECONOMIC AND INDUSTRIAL UNDERSTANDING - Aspects of industry are reflected in the *Science from the World of Work* units.
CAREERS EDUCATION AND GUIDANCE - Outside visits and visitors to the school can provide children with access to work places and the different roles of people in employment. Suggestions are included where appropriate.
HEALTH EDUCATION - A range of issues from the misuse of substances and safety, to the effect of the environment on health are tackled in the activities.
CITIZENSHIP - Activities which introduce the world of work, environmental concerns, etc occur throughout **Science in Action**.
ENVIRONMENTAL EDUCATION - Increased knowledge and understanding of the environment and the effect of human influences on the environment are highlighted in many activities.

SAFETY IN SCIENCE IN ACTION - 5 to 16

*Children involved in an investigation from **Swiss Family Robinson**
produced their own safety procedures.*

Throughout **Science in Action - 5 to 16** stress is laid on the importance of safety. Where
appropriate, safety issues are indicated in the teacher's notes and pupil activity pages. However, the responsibility for safety is delegated to the children, under the close supervision of the
teacher.

■ 'Teachers should encourage a <u>working understanding</u>
of safety and care.'* Under the teacher's direction
children need to make their <u>own</u> <u>decisions</u> about
safety.

■ Motivation to follow their own safety
procedures is probably higher than for those
imposed by adults. Children are very strict
with each other over their own rules.

■ The children should be asked to formulate their own
safety guidelines and explain their procedures to an
adult, who may then point out omissions, or suggest
alternatives before the children are allowed to
continue.

■ If they are not permitted to begin an activity until
they have described their safety procedures,
pupils have to take an overview of the whole
activity, plan ahead, anticipate problems and
suggest solutions.

■ Pupils need to examine the reasons why safety procedures are required before they can produce effective
measures to ensure their own investigation is safe.
They are more likely to appreciate and understand the
need for safety if they have had to consider the reasons
for themselves.

Additional safety information can be found in:
BE SAFE! ASE Publications, ASE, College Lane, Hatfield, Herts.

* National Curriculum Science for ages 5 to 16 (May 1991) Proposals of the Secretary of State for
Education and Science and the Secretary of State for Wales

USING SCIENCE IN ACTION - 5 TO 16

Science in Action - 5 to 16 is designed to provide support for the teacher from the initial planning stage of a topic right through to the conclusion of pupil's work and its assessment. The information on this and the following page explains the various sections within the scheme and how they support both teachers and children.

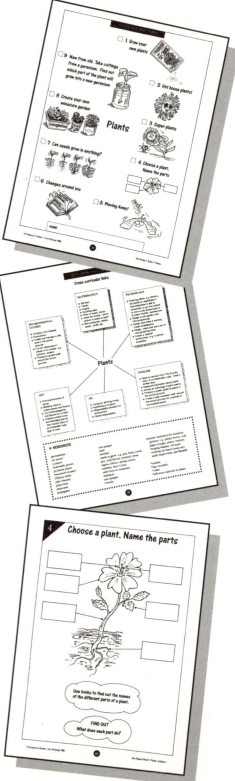

▶ ACTIVITY CHOICE PAGE

The activity choice page provides the teacher and pupils with an overview of the science activities within that unit. Each unit contains six core activities which are designed to be followed in sequence to develop understanding in concepts and investigations in a logical manner. Each unit also has three supplementary activities which can be used for reinforcement or for those who finish early. The activity choice page can be photocopied and given to groups or individuals to record progress through the unit.

▶ CROSS-CURRICULAR LINKS AND RESOURCES PAGE

This page is designed to show, at a glance:

- suggestions which facilitate a cross-curricular approach to the topic and provide assistance at the planning stage in the form of a cross-curricular flow diagram which indicates mathematics, English and, where appropriate, R.E. and foundation subjects.

- resources and equipment required for the unit. Specialised equipment, e.g. cameras and tape recorders, are highlighted at the end of the resources list.

▶ PUPILS' PAGES

The pupils' pages offer, where appropriate:
- stimulating artwork to motivate and provide clues to help pupils carry out the activity.
- a question or a problem for the children to solve.
- 'Did you know...' boxes with interesting facts or background information to help the children with the activity.
- suggestions for recording and communicating.

▶ TEACHER'S NOTES

Each activity is accompanied by a comprehensive set of teacher's notes. Where appropriate these notes include:

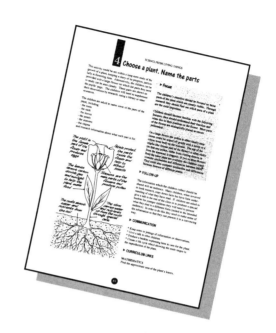

SAFETY INFORMATION
- The scheme aims to develop in children a working understanding of safety issues. Relevant information is provided for the teacher.

USEFUL STARTING POINTS
- This section provides suggestions for introducing the activities.

FOCUS BOX
- The shaded section contains the main focus of the activity in terms of developing pupils' knowledge and understanding, or skills and strategies in investigations. Although there may be different outcomes from any one activity, the focus box addresses a particular point which the teacher can develop with pupils.

VARIABLES
- Some activities which involve children in identifying and handling variables have a section in which the appropriate independent, dependent and control variables are given.

FOLLOW-UP
- The teacher can use the information in this section to develop the main activity or introduce further related tasks.

COMMUNICATION
- This section offers a wide range of methods for recording and communicating - appropriate to each activity. Communication has a high profile within this scheme; it is through communication that teachers can gain access to evidence for assessment. Hence the suggestions are frequently tailored to provide specific information which presents assessment points.

CURRICULUM LINKS
- These focus on aspects within each core subject which can be assessed. The information relates either directly to statements of attainment or the relevant programme of study and will provide specific opportunities for assessment.

USING THE UNITS IN SCIENCE IN ACTION - 5 TO 16

▶ **INTRODUCING THE UNIT**

There are many different ways to approach science in the classroom. The following suggestions are based on two of the units from **Science in Action - 5 to 16.**

JAMES AND THE GIANT PEACH

Starting points:
- class story
- taped serial
- paired or group reading
- individual reading.

THE PLAYGROUND

Starting points:
- class visit to a local playground
- discussion on children's views on parks and play areas
- survey of favourite play equipment
- interview someone from the Parks Department or an architect.

MANAGEMENT

Decide on class and group management:
- will all class members be engaged in science activities, or will groups carry out a range of activities from other areas of the curriculum at the same time?
- ensure that group sizes are not too large for the activity
- check the teacher's notes for useful suggestions and the focus of each science activity
- decide whether any of the activities will be used for assessment purposes.

DEFINE THE TASK

Allow the children time to discuss and define the tasks before they begin. Check that children understand their task before they begin.

CARRYING OUT THE ACTIVITY

Groups should be encouraged, with support, to make their own decisions about how to carry out the activity. They should also be allowed to change their minds during the activity if they feel it is necessary. The group size should enable each member to have some responsibility.

The central part of the activity will be collecting data, and making sense of it.

FEEDBACK

Feedback after each activity, directly to the teacher or indirectly, via a different audience, is essential. This is one of the main opportunities the teacher has to help children refine concepts and discuss the quality of the strategies they employed to answer their question or solve their problem.

WHERE NEXT?

With support from the teacher the children might generate a new set of questions, arising from their activity, which they could explore. Alternatively, they should be directed to the next activity.

CONCLUDING A UNIT

Although children should record and communicate as they work sometimes it can be fun, as well as good practice, to produce a class display, conference, etc. This provides a focus for discussion about different ways of working and the strengths and weaknesses of different forms of recording.

JAMES AND THE GIANT PEACH

The children could re-tell the story in a display, introducing at relevant points information they have gained either from investigations or research. For example, they might produce a series of newspaper reports following the adventures of the peach and its inhabitants. These might include an article describing sightings of a flying peach which could make references to their own data from the parachute investigation. The children could include an explanation, for example, of how a peach can stay in the air using a parachute.

Another article might be headlined 'Our intrepid reporter talks to Miss Spider about her eventful life'.

THE PLAYGROUND

During this unit children will have designed, constructed and tested their own working model of a playground. This could provide the focus of an exhibition about the playground, with relevant information about the designs, materials, structures and the results of their tests. Their accounts could be word-processed or tape-recorded to complement the models.

Invitations could be sent to other classes, parents and representatives of the Parks Department to attend a presentation given by the class. This presentation could include demonstrations and talks, with children acting as guides for visitors viewing the exhibition.

GROUP WORK IN SCIENCE - 5 TO 16

Working within a group is an important aspect of life in general. Science is an area of the curriculum where children are invariably asked to work together. They need to develop the ability to function cooperatively within a group situation.

The most popular methods of organisation are the whole class:
1. in groups involved in the same science activity
2. in groups engaged in different science activities
3. in groups participating in a range of cross-curricular activities.

■ it fosters co-operation

■ children support each other, encouraging perseverance

■ pupils share ideas, responsibilities and problems

■ children can refine their own ideas in the light of other people's ideas and experiences

ADVANTAGES OF GROUP WORK

■ it encourages peer-tutoring; children teach each other, e.g. how to use digital scales

■ children stimulate each other to produce ideas

■ children learn to delegate

■ children learn to appreciate the attributes and abilities of others.

▶ THE INFLUENCE OF GROUP SIZE

One of the most important influences on classroom management and the success of any science investigation is the size of the groups working together.

The optimum size for a group is 3 - 4 children. The reasons for this are straightforward. The larger the group, the greater the risk of redundant children. Redundant children are most likely to become bored and become a source of discipline problems.

Most science investigations only offer three or four roles for children within a group:

- someone to record
- someone to measure.
- someone to get the equipment
- someone to do the testing } these are often combined

Small groups benefit from the fact that each child is more likely to have a specific role and be able to make a useful contribution.

However, it is important to realise that there are times when children will prefer to work individually and this should be accommodated whenever possible.

It is also important that teachers know when to intervene. For example, where a group situation is breaking down, the teacher might have to:
- change the dynamics of the group
- suggest roles for the children
- discuss the problem but insist that the children resolve their differences

EQUAL ACCESS IN SCIENCE IN ACTION - 5 to 16

> 'The entitlement of all pupils to a broad curriculum is embodied in the core and foundation subjects: this being regardless of race, gender, disability or geographical location.'*

- If both boys and girls develop positive images of themselves in science it can help to counter comments such as:

  - 'Only boys can be scientists, girls aren't clever enough.' **

- Pupils should be encouraged to see themselves engaged in science. Photographs of children working in science displayed around the classroom can help to promote a positive image.

- Some children, often girls or less confident pupils, stand back and reflect on an investigation. This is sometimes seen as disinterest. Encourage these children to share their ideas and suggestions.

- Many children adopt the same role during every investigation. Ensure that children rotate roles from one investigation to another.

- Some roles, such as measuring using a stop watch, are more popular than others. Often the more dominant child commandeers this role. It is important that children have access to all roles from using a stop watch to recording data.

- Many children, for whatever reason, have difficulty with reading and writing, and this can place them at a disadvantage in science. Inability to cope with written or spoken language should not be equated with an inability to cope in science.

- Some children prefer to work alone, following their own ideas and strategies. Although the social implications of group work are important opportunities for working alone should not be overlooked.

- Although the level and amount of language on the pupils' pages in Science In Action - 5 to 16 has been kept deliberately low, some children will require support. Suggestions for additional support include:
  - Tape record the question from the pupils' page so that children can listen to the question but still use the illustrations on the page for clues.
  - Photocopy, cut and paste the pupils' activity sheet to create a version tailored to the needs of the individual or group.
  - Allow children access to instructions in the form of strip cartoons produced by other pupils. This provides valuable assistance while at the same time it provides an audience for another pupil's work.
  - Where necessary simplify instructions or talk through activity sheets with children.

- The familiar contexts of activities in **Science in Action - 5 to 16** can help to motivate many children.

- Encourage children to ask their own questions. Motivation is high when children are allowed to follow their own ideas and work at their own level of ability.

- The activities allow the teacher to differentiate by outcome in terms of assessment. This means that children of various abilities will be able to access and carry out activities at their own level of ability.

- Follow-up material throughout **Science in Action - 5 to 16** takes account of differing work rates of children in a class.

- Invite visitors into the classroom to help children to appreciate that a variety of people in the community rely on science, from the baker to the pharmacist.

- Invite other adults into the classroom to support pupils particularly with reading and recordings.

---

*   N.C.C.   Curriculum Guidance 3 - *A Curriculum For All*
* * Information from research by Parveen Ahmed - Cleveland Multicultural Development Team.

ACTIVITIES IN SCIENCE IN ACTION - 5 TO 16

Throughout **Science in Action - 5 to 16** pupils are engaged in a variety of activities which allow access to the different parts of the science curriculum; from using reference books to researching information about the solar system, to making decisions about variables when carrying out an investigation.

OBSERVATION

Observation is central to science. It provides the connection between what pupils have learned and the outside world. Throughout this scheme children engage in a range of activities involving observation, such as watching a snail to find out how it moves, or feeling the texture of different soils.

Pupils are also required to quantify some observations, for example rainfall amounts in a weather investigation.

RESEARCH

Not all things in science can be investigated in the classroom. Children need to use a range of reference material to extend their knowledge and understanding of the natural and physical world. This allows them access to more detailed information, like the names and purposes of parts of a flower.

INVESTIGATIONS

Not all science activities are investigations. Investigations have a specific format which involve children in:
- making their own decisions
- planning for themselves
- identifying and handling variables
- finding their own route to a solution
- deciding what equipment and resources they need
- refining concepts which they already understand.

INSTRUCTIONS

Instructions are used in an enabling capacity. Children are occasionally asked to follow a set of instructions, for example how to make recycled paper or bake bread. Such items can then be used as the basis for a series of investigations.

SECONDARY DATA AND SURVEYS

Many activities require children to handle data produced by other people. Here children have to make sense of secondary data without the background knowledge gained from having carried out the activity. They should be able to evaluate the credibility of the information, as well as draw conclusions. Children also need to be able to carry out their own surveys in a variety of contexts, e.g. investigating waste paper or the habitats of spiders around the school.

TRY IT AND SEE

Children of all ages will need to engage in 'try it and see' activities. This is where children try out an idea on an informal basis to see what happens. Often this becomes part of an investigation where children decide they need to have a dummy run to see how a certain idea works. When making a model children sometimes try out a number of alternatives before incorporating one of them into their overall design. Pupils need to be confident that this type of activity will be valued and given time.

▶ DEVELOPING INVESTIGATIONS

Investigation should make up about 50% of all science activities carried out by children. The following pages provide support for the teacher in understanding and developing different aspects of investigations in science.

WHAT DOES AN INVESTIGATION LOOK LIKE?

Investigations do have a basic format but, depending on the ability of the pupil, different aspects will be employed more successfully than others. For example, many children are competent at creating a fair test but have difficulty collecting, recording and making sense of numerical data.

Some pupils will take a systematic approach to investigations, planning carefully at the beginning, others will move straight into the activity, handling problems as and when they arise. The examples that follow are taken from 'Hold the peach up!' (*James and the Giant Peach*, Key Stage 2 Book 2).

THE INVESTIGATION CYCLE

■ During feedback, when the teacher gently probes pupils' understanding of forces, discussion might lead to further ideas. The children might say that the weight is important. How could they test whether the weight of the peach affects how quickly it falls? They could be encouraged to think up further questions which could be investigated, such as:
- does the weight of the peach or the shape of the parachute affect how long it takes it to fall?

■ The opportunity to report what they have done, their results and conclusions to other people is important. This feedback helps the children to make sense of what they have done and contributes to the process of refining concepts. In this activity they would focus on the properties of materials and the forces which affect how the parachute falls. The teacher's role in asking questions is crucial at this stage.

■ Having completed their investigation children need to decide what their results mean. This might include noting the best and worst materials or placing the times in order. It should also include looking at the way in which the investigation was carried out and reviewing the results critically. Children should ask the question, 'Can these results be believed?'

■ Initially children are given a question or a problem. Alternatively they might generate their own ideas which can be tested.

James and the Giant Peach
Science in Action Key Stage 2 Book 2

■ Results are recorded in a simple table (or by other methods). This helps children to organise the data so that they can make use of it later. They could glue samples of material in the appropriate column.

Material	Time

■ Children should define the task, deciding what it means. It is important that the teacher discusses the groups' interpretations to make sure that pupils are on an acceptable course and have not totally misunderstood what the question is asking. However sometimes learning is more powerful when children are allowed to work through their own ideas and find out at the end that they did not collect the data that they needed. Discussion can then help the children appreciate why, and consider alternatives.

■ Pupils then plan how to tackle the investigation, exchanging ideas, deciding which route to take, or who will be responsible for which tasks. Some roles, such as using a stopwatch, are invariably more popular than others, children need to learn to negotiate with each other.

■ In their planning children have to make decisions concerning variables such as:
- how many different types of materials?
- what size should the parachute be?
- how much Plasticine?
- how many times should it be dropped?
- how will we time it?

■ Next, children carry out their test by making a parachute and dropping it three times, using a stopwatch to time the falls. Some children use the middle value as a rough average, others carry out calculations. Many children do not realise at the beginning that the height from which they are dropping the parachute is too low for them to be able to time the fall. This means they have to start again and drop the parachute from a greater height.

VARIABLES IN INVESTIGATIONS

As children progress through their science education they are expected to engage in a wide range of activities. Investigations are one of the most important and demanding of these activities.

One important feature of investigations is children's ability to identify and handle variables of increasing complexity. Although pupils would not be expected to use terminology such as 'independent', 'dependent' and 'control variables', it is important, for assessment purposes, that the teacher recognises the different variables and the role they play in investigations.

Throughout **Science in Action -5 to 16** the teacher's notes assist the teacher by identifying the relevant variables where appropriate.

▶ WHAT ARE VARIABLES?

In an investigation variables are the things that the children decide to either change or keep the same. The following example is again set in the context of an investigation about parachutes.

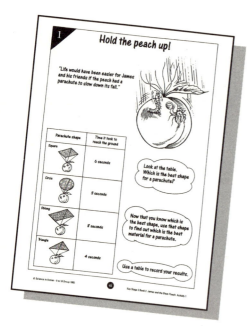

Which is the best material for a parachute?

CONTROL VARIABLES

These are the things that the children decide must be kept the same throughout the investigation. They should realise that their test would be unfair if some things were not controlled such as:
- size of the canopy
- number of strings
- weight
- shape.

Sometimes children find it difficult to decide which aspects to control and if, for example, they decided to control colour the teacher would be right to question their understanding of fair tests.

DEPENDENT VARIABLE

The dependent variable is the outcome; it depends on what happens during the test. Usually this requires some kind of measurement. In this investigation the dependent variable would be the length of time the parachute takes to fall.

Children should be encouraged to quantify the dependent variable and use tables to record measurements.

Children should also be reminded to choose appropriate units, and label them. Writing 35 without the unit could mean 35mm, 35cm or 35 elephants.

INDEPENDENT VARIABLE

The independent variable is the thing that children decide to change systematically. This will be determined by the question or problem and pupils will need to recognise whether they should measure time, length, capacity, weight, etc. In this case it is the type of material used for the parachute canopy, e.g. paper, polythene, fabric.

The clue to the independent variable is in the question, i.e. 'Which is the **best** material?' In this case the independent variable is the **type** of material, but the children will have to decide what is meant here by 'best'. In this particular investigation the 'best' is undoubtedly the material which allows the parachute to fall in the slowest time.

Independent, dependent and control variables can be:

■ **Categoric** - where the variable is a category, i.e. a colour or a shape or, for example, which is the best **material** for a parachute?

■ **Discrete** - where the value of the variable is a whole number only, e.g. how many holes should a parachute have 1, 2, 3 or 4?

■ **Continuous** - the variable can have any value, e.g. 1, 1.2, 1.4, 1.6. If the children were to investigate how the weight of the Plasticine affects the fall of the parachute the weights involved might not be whole numbers, e.g. 1g, 1.5g, 2g, etc..

■ **Derived** - where the dependent variable is calculated from more than one measurement, for example, the **speed** of the parachute is derived (obtained) from measurements of **distance** and **time**. For example, the speed of a parachute moving 3 metres in 2 seconds is 1.5 metres per second.

▶ VARIABLES AND GRAPHS

The type of variables involved has an effect on the type of tables and graphs children should use to display their data. Again, using the parachute activity from *James and the Giant Peach* as an example, if children were to investigate the following questions the different variables would require different types of graph as shown in the table below.

Investigation	Type of variable	Type of graph
What is the best shape for a parachute?	Categoric	Bar graph
What is the best material for a parachute?	Categoric (material)	Bar graph
How many holes should a parachute have?	Discrete (number of holes, e.g. 1, 2, 3, 4)	Bar graph
How does the weight affect the fall of a parachute?	Continuous (weight, e.g. 1g, 1.5g, 2g, 2.5g)	Line graph

EFFECTIVE QUESTIONING IN INVESTIGATIONS

One of the central themes of **Science in Action - 5 to 16** is the importance of effective questioning. Throughout the scheme children are encouraged to generate their own questions, and opportunities for questioning by the teacher to introduce ideas, refine concepts and develop procedures in investigations are highlighted.

Teachers should: 'Encourage the raising and answering of questions.' *

■ question the validity of data generated by themselves, and by other people

■ develop the ability to generate a range of questions

■ be able to question each other in a critical manner

Children should:

■ understand that different types of questions can be answered in different ways

■ appreciate that some questions have more than one answer

■ be able to reorganise which questions can be answered through investigations

■ be able to support answers to questions, where necessary, using data from investigations

■ develop appropriate strategies to answer different types of questions

► ENCOURAGING QUESTIONS

It is essential that children feel confident that their questions will be well received and that they will be given the opportunity to answer them. Equally important is the help children require to recognise different types of questions.

Teachers can encourage children to ask their own questions if they:
■ tape record questions
■ brainstorm a list of questions
■ create 20 questions 'All the things you want to know about...'
■ create a class question board
■ produce a class or group question book
■ store questions in a computer data base
■ produce a bank of questions which children can add to as well as answer.

► CLASSIFYING QUESTIONS

| Questions which can be answered using reference material, e.g. how does a snail move? | Questions which can be answered by further observation, e.g. which type of food does a snail like best? | Questions which can be investigated (a fair test), e.g. 'Which type of food does a snail like best?' |

* National Curriculum Science for ages 5-16 (May 1991) Proposals of the Secretary of State for Education and Science and the Secretary of State for Wales

Asking the right question, at the right time, while children are involved in an investigation is one of the more difficult aspects of science teaching. Questions need to be framed in a supportive manner which encourages children to be critical of their own work.

Below are suggestions for questions which might be asked at various stages of an investigation.

▶ EVALUATING
Can you think of ways you could improve your test?
If you could do it again which part would you change?

▶ CONCLUDING
What have you found out?
Were you right?
Why do you think that happened?
How can you prove that you are right?

▶ HANDLING DATA
You have some interesting results. What do you notice?
Can you see a pattern in your results?
What do you think has happened? Why?
What caused that?

▶ SOLVING PROBLEMS
Is there something wrong?
Can you think why that is happening?
What do you think the problem is?
What makes you think that it is the problem?
Does it matter? Why?
How will you solve your problem?
Does anyone else have an idea?
Which idea do you think you should try?

▶ MEASURING/OBSERVING
What are you trying to find out?
What will you use to measure in your investigation? Why?
Why have you chosen to use that?
Is there any change?
Will one measurement be enough?

▶ DEFINING THE TASK
What are you trying to do?
What do you think you have got to do?
What do you think the question means?

▶ HYPOTHESISING
Why do you think that will happen?
Can you think of a reason why it might do that?

QUESTIONS DURING INVESTIGATIONS

▶ PREDICTING
What do you think will happen?
Which one do you think will be best?
Can you put them in order before you test them?

▶ PLANNING
Has everyone shared their ideas?
Have you decided what to do?
Who is going to do what?
Why have you decided to do it that way?
Can you see any problems?
What will happen if you use that idea?

▶ HANDLING VARIABLES
How have you made this a fair test?
What have you kept the same?
What have you changed?
What are you going to measure?
How could you make it fair?
Does it matter how you do that?

PROGRESSION IN INVESTIGATIONS

Four main strands can be identified in investigations, the following table suggests progression through five levels in each of the strands.

	QUESTIONS	CARRYING OUT
1	Questions are central to science. At this early stage the teacher will need to support children by providing models of question forms such as: - what will happen? - how can? - why? - what if?	Children develop simple strategies to try out their ideas and see what happens. Observation at this level is mainly qualitative, but there is some movement towards using non-standard measurement.
2	Children are more able and confident in suggesting their own ideas and ask a wide range of questions with increasingly less support from the teacher.	The teacher encourages children to appreciate the need for keeping things fair in their tests. Children progress towards using standard measurements. They begin to cope with working in a group and allocating responsibilities.
3	Pupils should be able to recognise which questions and ideas can be tested by an investigation. Many of the ideas and predictions generated by children will be the indirect result of other investigations.	Children should be able to recognise whether a test is fair - this can occur at any stage of an investigation, at the planning stage, during the investigation or while evaluating the outcome.
4	Children should be able to use their knowledge and understanding to suggest ideas and questions which can be tested. Brainstorming within a group or class is a useful procedure for generating ideas. Further questions also emerge when children analyse data and draw conclusions at the end of an investigation.	At this stage children should be able to construct and carry out fair tests. Pupils should be able to recognise and handle key variables and make measurements using appropriate equipment.
5	Pupils should be able to base their hypotheses on links between cause and effect, based on their personal knowledge and understanding.	Fair tests become increasingly sophisticated, demanding that pupils manipulate variables to ensure that the results of their investigation are accurate and valid.

	RECORDING	CONCLUSION AND EVALUATION
1	Children classify data into sets using an increasing range of criteria. Gradually children move towards ordering, e.g. largest to smallest. Simple oral accounts of activities provide complementary information.	The teacher needs to help children link their observations to the original question or idea. Children should be invited to use their personal understanding to make sense of their observations. It is important that children begin to try to interpret or explain, making connections between knowledge and observation.
2	Children should be able to construct and use tables to record qualitative and quantitative observations. Accounts of investigations might be oral, written or pictorial, describing the salient points.	Having placed information in tables children should attempt to make sense of the data. They should be able to note best, worst, similarities and differences and, where appropriate, order data. Children should be able to use their results to support their conclusions.
3	Pupils should be able to construct and use tables to record measurements and observations. They should be able to give a sequential account of the salient features.	Pupils should appreciate that to make their results believable a fair test is necessary. They should also recognise the necessity for numerical data. Data should be used to help justify their conclusions.
4	Data should be organised using tables and, where appropriate, information represented in a bar chart.	Pupils should be able to recognise patterns and relationships in data. Data should be used to support conclusions and predictions.
5	Pupils are able to use a combination of recording methods to describe and explain their investigation. Using ordered prose, tables, graphs, diagrams etc., children can communicate different parts of an activity.	Pupils should be able to reflect critically on how an investigation was carried out. They should be able to recognise whether their test has produced a valid set of results from which useful conclusions can be drawn.

DATA COLLECTION IN INVESTIGATIONS

The generation and handling of data is central to investigations in science. It provides the evidence on which children can base their conclusions, make predictions and raise further questions. By analysing and interpreting the data children are able to refine and develop their understanding of basic concepts.

Pupils should appreciate that, if their results and conclusions are to be believed, subjective judgements are insufficient - their data must be able to withstand scrutiny. This means that they must generate numerical data. However the generation of numerical data alone is insufficient. Children must develop an understanding of the value of data. They need to be able to make sense of the numbers they have produced.

As children progress in science they should develop an increasing understanding that numerical data can:
- provide evidence of what happened
- show patterns in results
- help them to come to conclusions
- allow them to make predictions
- generate opportunities for further questions
- provide opportunities for them to challenge other people's conclusions and predictions.

The generation of useful data depends on the pupils' ability to handle variables in an investigation. However it should be remembered that in some investigations qualitative observations also provide essential information, e.g. changes in colour, texture, smell, etc.

▶ WHICH IS THE BEST MEASURING EQUIPMENT?

If children are always given the correct equipment they will never need to make their own decisions about which measuring instrument is the most appropriate to the task. They need to decide whether to use:
- a metre stick or a centimetre ruler
- a 2 litre jug or a 100cm³ cylinder
- a stop clock or digital stop watch
- kitchen scales or digital scales.

Pupils also have to decide how accurate their measurements need to be.

▶ WHEN SHOULD MEASUREMENTS BE MADE?

Children will have to make a range of decisions such as:

- how many measurements do I need to make?
- should I repeat the measurements?
- when do I start and finish measuring?
- how often do I make measurements, e.g. every 10 cm, 15 cm, etc.
- will I have enough measurements to be able to make sense of them? Will there be enough to show a pattern?

▶ THE VALUE OF MEASUREMENTS

The use of measurement is important in helping children to:
- answer the original question
- make predictions
- substantiate conclusions
- generate new questions.

Numerical data gives children access to:
- best value
- worst value
- intermediate value
- changes in data
- patterns
- relationships between one set of measurements and another.

▶ ORGANISING MEASUREMENTS

During many investigations children will generate a large amount of data. The organisation of data is important, children should develop an understanding of how careful organisation and display can help them. They should be able to:
- place data in a table
- order the results
- recognise when to represent the data in a bar chart or graph.

CHILDREN RECORDING AND ASSESSMENT OPPORTUNITIES

Primary science is fun; it is exciting and varied. In contrast, children's recording in primary science has traditionally taken the form of the written word, which can be tedious, limiting and in many cases inappropriate to the activity. For children with language difficulties using writing as the main method of recording their science work severely disadvantages them. Science has much to offer language development (see section on Writing, page 24) but the main purpose of children's recording should be to add to the value of the science.

Asking children to record everything they do in science is totally unnecessary. Children should be allowed to experience the unusual, exciting and beautiful, without having to make a record of it. Where children record in science it should be because it is useful to the activity and the child. The need to record, and the most appropriate method to use, will vary with the activity.

A wide range of recording methods, specifically chosen to match each activity, are suggested throughout the scheme.

▶ COMMUNICATION

Children's findings and ideas should be open to questions and challenged by other children and adults. Communication is crucial in science. It is through communication that children begin to make sense of the data they have collected, clarify their ideas and begin to draw conclusions, as well as develop language skills. The quality of questions asked, particularly by the teacher, can help to reveal the extent of a child's depth of understanding.

Communication also plays a role in encouraging pupils to listen to the opinions of others and to consider that other people's way of working and outcomes are as valid as their own. If they learn to listen to other children pupils might modify their own ideas or adopt strategies used by others which they consider useful.

WHY DO CHILDREN NEED TO RECORD?

DATA COLLECTION

Recording is necessary to deal with data collection in an efficient manner, particularly when dealing with numerical data. Tables, for example, present information in a way that makes it easily accessible.

RECOGNISING PATTERNS

Children need to record numerical data so that they can recognise patterns in their information which will help them in their interpretation. For example, in an investigation into how the different ply of a yarn affects its strength, children recognise a pattern that suggests that the 4 ply yarn is twice as strong as 2 ply.

APPRECIATING LONG-TERM CHANGE

Pupils need to be given the opportunity to collect and store data over long periods of time, which can then be used to analyse and interpret change by looking for relationships, and cause and effect. Allowing children to accumulate data about the mini-environments around school each season is a profitable exercise as they can then develop an understanding about seasonal changes, links between environmental factors and types of plants and animals. Another excellent example of recording long-term change is children's growth. Information collected on an annual basis can be stored in a computer data base. The accumulated data provides an excellent resource for work on growth patterns and questions which link for example height with shoe size, gender, etc.

APPRECIATING SHORT-TERM CHANGE

Sudden changes, for example when a material is heated, or sugar dissolved, also need to be recorded. Qualitative observations can be in the form of notes, tape recordings or photographs, all of which then allow children to reflect on the changes and develop concepts related to cause and effect.

RECOGNISING CYCLES

Too often children note change, particularly long-term change, but are not given enough time to relate their observations to recurring patterns or cycles. Repeating observations of the moon over two or three months will help children to come to terms with the cyclical nature of the phases of the moon.
Computer records of weather information allow older children to analyse data and suggest patterns and relationships, e.g. wind direction and temperature.

ASSISTING PLANNING

Several methods of recording can function as 'organisers', for example tables.

ASSESSMENT OPPORTUNITIES

Recording provides tangible evidence of children's ability not only in science but also for maths and English. Evidence can range from a motor-driven model vehicle with working headlights to a written account of an investigation where children describe a fair test.

A range of methods of recording are suggested on the following pages. Since children's recording often provides the teacher with tangible evidence for assessment, examples of how certain methods might offer assessment points have been included where appropriate.

Although a range of recording is essential it is important that this is not used only as a context for written work or art. Developing skills across the curriculum is vital, but it is **not** science.

COLLAGES

Children might produce a collage, based on accurate observations of, for example, a tree. The collage could be made from a wide variety of appropriate materials and might indicate changes through the seasons, providing information about:
- birds and invertebrates which use the tree as a habitat
- types and colours of leaves
- bark patterns
- canopy shape.

Additional information could be placed around the collage, such as:
- tree dimensions
- shadow
- photographs of the tree through the day and the seasons
- researched information about the life cycle of the tree.

Where information has been included about food chains this would provide a useful assessment point.

COLLECTIONS

Collections can indicate the level of understanding if children are asked to make or classify their collection according to certain criteria.

Assessment points might include collections of materials suitable as insulators and conductors in electric circuits, or objects classified as biodegradable and non-biodegradable.

COMPUTERS

Computers can be used by children themselves, or by children dictating to an adult, to:
- handle data in tables
- represent information in graphs
- store information collected over extended periods of time, e.g. weather statistics
- word-process accounts of investigations
- word-process information from reference material.

Computers help to take away the tedium of producing tables and graphs, allowing children to handle data more quickly.

DIAGRAMS

Diagrams are simple pictures with labels or explanations. They can be used to 'fill in the gaps', complementing a table or writing and providing additional information about an activity.

Children could produce 'before' and 'after' diagrams when making working models. Annotations might indicate:
- reasons for using specific materials
- the function of different parts of the model
- problems encountered while making the model
- solutions to problems
- modifications to the original design.

Diagrammatic representations of electric circuits are useful assessment points. Children might be asked to create a diagram of a working circuit for a friend to make. If successful, this indicates an understanding of circuit construction.

GRAPHS

Graphs are used to represent data in a form which helps children to:
- note patterns in numerical data
- recognise extremes in data
- compare several sets of data more easily
- note changes.

MODELS

It is important that models in science serve a purpose. They should either be working models, or they should record observations made by the children. In the unit on *James and the Giant Peach* children could be asked to make a model spider. The teacher should demand accurate observation of:
- structure
- colour
- shape
- features.

If children are asked to recreate a spider's habitat in which to place the model this adds another dimension. Children might supplement the scene with sketches, poetry, or information from books about spiders.

Models incorporating electric circuits provide useful assessment opportunities in electricity.

NOTES

Notes can be a mixture of writing, tables, pictures, symbols etc., whichever the child finds most useful.

Notes serve as an aide-memoire, reminding the children of:
- the sequence of events
- happenings
- amusing moments
- surprises
- problems
- changes.

Notes are personal jottings, they should be free from the teacher's red pen.

ORAL WORK

Children should be given an audience, with whom they can share their ideas and report their investigations. This might be individually or in a group to:
- the teacher
- other children
- a helper
- visitors.

When children are asked to speak to others they should be given a clear outline of what is expected and time to plan and prepare a presentation. They should consider their audience and be challenged to think in terms of focusing their attention on the most important aspects of their work. The teacher should demand that children:
- order their thoughts
- be concise
- use information appropriately
- ensure that each member of the group has a role
- be prepared to be challenged and answer questions.

PHOTOGRAPHS

Photographs can illustrate long- and short-term change, or a sequence of events. For example, children might be involved in a project to transform part of the school grounds into a wild area or a vegetable patch. A camera would help to record the stages in the transformation. Eventually a photographic display by the children would provide an excellent record, particularly if complemented by a range of other methods of recording such as:
- ordered prose
- poetry
- stories
- accounts of problems and solutions.

Photographs, accompanied by explanations, which show a sequence of changes related to baking bread could provide assessment of pupils' understanding of the action of heat on everyday substances.

PICTURES

These could include:
- sketches
- paintings
- advertisements
- posters.

An annotated drawing of the parts of a flower would provide an assessment point.

PRINTING

This is an excellent technique for recording observations. It allows most children, even those with limited artistic skills, to produce a recognisable picture. The picture should be accompanied by written observations, or reactions to the subject, or the results of literature research such as information about snails.

STRIP CARTOONS

This method combines language and pictures. Children use paper divided into 4 - 8 frames. Each frame should be filled with a picture, and perhaps sentences describing part of their investigation. A strip cartoon could assess children's ability to produce a sequential account of the salient points of an activity.

TAPE RECORDING

Encourage children to use a tape recorder to record:
- observations
- their own questions
- their own instructions for others to use
- sound in the environment
- interviews
- simulations of real life situations, for example a radio weather forecast.

A recording of an explanation to accompany a model of the solar system provides an assessment of children's understanding of the relationship between the sun and the planets.

BOOKS

Children can create their own books to describe their investigations, or to record information from research. Challenge children to include a range of recording methods, for example writing, sketches, diagrams, photographs, tables and graphs.
Insist that children use a real book format, with a contents page, a simple index if appropriate, and an intriguing front cover.

CRITIQUE

This type of written work challenges children to analyse their investigation, encouraging them to be critical of their own work. This allows the teacher to assess children's ability to reflect critically, commenting on:
- difficulties they encountered
- things that went wrong
- surprises
- things of interest
- changes and improvements
- alternative approaches
- whether the fair test was effective.

DESCRIPTIONS

Descriptions of observations or investigations do not always have to be in ordered prose, insistence on good sentence structure can often inhibit children. Alternatives might include lists of words, phrases or tape-recorded descriptions.

INSTRUCTIONS

It is important for children to have an audience for their writing. It helps to focus their attention and make them take into account the needs of the person or people receiving the information. Asking children to create a set of instructions for someone else to use is an excellent use of writing.
Instructions:
- give writing a purpose
- help children to place events in sequence
- require precision
- require concise statements
- should be used by other children
- can be fun to write and use.
For children with language difficulties oral or pictorial instructions are equally valid.

LETTERS

Science can provide realistic contexts for letter writing. The teacher should ask children to collect data from their investigation and present it in an appropriate letter format. Letters can be written to:
- obtain information from a range of agencies
- complain about environmental problems
- suggest solutions to problems to appropriate authorities
- describe to manufacturers how investigations into their products were carried out.

LISTS

Lists are particularly useful when children are classifying data and have to note similarities and differences. For example the unit called 'Speedy Gonzales' in Book 4 asks children to make a list of the positive features of motor vehicles as a form of transport. Lists can then be displayed and discussed with the rest of the class.

NEWSPAPERS

Many computer programs enable children to produce newspaper pages. Children might describe their investigations in the form of a column for the 'Science Today' section, or report on startling findings for a *Which* -type magazine article. It is important that children are given an audience and are challenged to decide what it is that the reader needs to know. For example in the unit 'Ahoy There!' children are invited to write about a rescue at sea in which they describe how a life-jacket design saved a person's life.
If the teacher demands that children explain why the lifejacket floats this provides access to an assessment point.

POETRY

Poems are a powerful vehicle for recording and communi-cating observations and emotions in science. Poems can be used to provide descriptions of investigations and to comment on issues such as pollution.

STORIES

Children can be challenged to use their knowledge and understanding within the context of a story. For example the unit on the *Swiss Family Robinson* in book 4, provides a great deal of scope for narrative writing, with the outcomes from investigations incorporated into the storyline. For example, the children might design and test a raft and then use this experience to write a story in which the family make a raft to use in an attempt to circumnavigate the island.

HELPING CHILDREN TO CREATE TABLES

The use of tables begins in Key Stage 1, with children producing sets for simple classification, e.g. floats/sinks, magnetic/non-magnetic, rough/smooth.

Sets are similar in structure to two-column tables, but the children are simply asked to place objects according to their characteristics.

Trays and boxes are, in effect, the beginnings of a table, as are work surfaces which have been divided using chalk, strips of paper or coloured tape.

The next step is to transfer these columns of objects to large pieces of paper - the beginnings of more formal tables. Children could draw around the objects, glue them on, use ticks and crosses or frowns and smiles. As children become more confident and competent at using tables they should be invited to produce, with help initially, a simple table of their own.

Pupils often have great difficulty constructing a table. Many children find it hard to juggle pencil and ruler on a piece of blank or lined paper. The use of large squared paper gives pupils guidelines to follow when they are drawing up the different parts of their table and this can be a help. Children should also be encouraged to consider a rough draft, since they may wish to re-arrange columns once they begin to work and their investigation starts to take shape. The final product may not emerge until the end of the activity.

Children should be given every opportunity to produce their own tables. A table produced by the teacher is less useful as it does not challenge the children to think about the investigation and the data they need to collect. It is also a good idea to allow pupils to produce something which they, personally, will find useful.

Type of sugar	Time to dissolve	How it dissolved
Brown sugar	58 seconds	Water went brown
Caster sugar	19 seconds	
Sugar cube	1 min 40 secs	Very slow, crumbled
Granulated sugar	40 seconds	
Demerara sugar	52 seconds	Water went golden
Icing sugar	We can't tell if it has dissolved	Water went cloudy

WHY ARE TABLES USEFUL?

A table is one of the most useful methods of recording which children can employ as it organises the data and is therefore of direct use during an investigation.

A table:

- controls the organisation of material and equipment
- helps to allocate responsibilities within a group
- indicates the need to control variables
- provides children with easy access to data
- helps to sequence actions
- encourages accurate observations
- defines the beginning and end of data collection
- sets out data in an orderly manner
- allows children to take an overall view of an investigation.

Tables should not be seen as an end product, they should be the beginning of a new set of procedures. Tables should be analysed, interpreted and conclusions drawn which might lead to a new hypothesis which can be tested.

For example the table shown here provides information about the fastest-dissolving sugar, which was the castor sugar. Pupils might hypothesise that, the finer the sugar, the more quickly it dissolves, and assume that by crushing the granulated sugar and quick-dissolving sugar cube, these will dissolve more quickly. They can then test this idea, or hypothesis.

Frequently children collect large amounts of data which they find difficult to analyse and interpret. Under these circumstances tabulated data could be re-presented as a graph, allowing patterns, relationships and change to be seen more clearly.

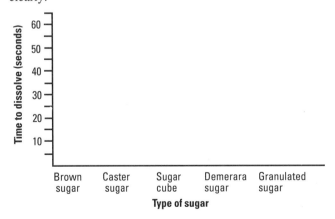

Children also need opportunities to use tables produced by other children - making sense of secondary data is an important skill in science. When children handle data generated by their own investigations they often draw conclusions by referring to the experience and do not use the data. To prevent children doing this they need to handle other people's data where they cannot fall back on personal knowledge.

ASSESSMENT IN SCIENCE IN ACTION - 5 TO 16

Formal assessment is becoming an established part of teaching and there are a variety of approaches to suit a range of situations. The flexible nature of **Science in Action - 5 to 16** allows the teacher to incorporate his or her own method of assessing children into the scheme but support is given in a number of different ways.

▶ WHAT TO ASSESS

The teacher's notes provide assessment opportunities in mathematics and English in the curriculum links sections.

An assessment grid indicates which science statements of attainment are covered by each activity, allowing the teacher to link directly to the National Curriculum as the example below shows.

▶ EVIDENCE FOR ASSESSMENT

The communication section of the teacher's notes suggests ways in which children can record and communicate in science. This provides evidence for assessment purposes. Sometimes the teacher will listen to an oral report, on other occasions children might produce, for example, a model which contains a working electric circuit, both of these activities would provide assessment points.
If the teacher keeps a notebook of observations this can also be very useful for assessment.

▶ RECORDING ASSESSMENT

A photocopiable assessment record sheet is provided on page 27 to record individual pupils progress through the National Curriculum. It is sub-divided to show individual level statements which help to indicate progress.

	Activity	Attainment Target 1 (scientific investigation)		Attainment Targets 2—4 (knowledge and understanding)	
		Programme of study	Statement of attainment	Programme of study	Statement of attainment
Core Units	1	Activities should help pupils to use and develop scientific knowledge and understanding	—	Pupils should explore friction	4,3c
	2	Activities should help pupils to use and develop scientific knowledge and understanding	—	Pupils should investigate the properties of magnetic and non-magnetic materials	4,2a
	3	Activities should help pupils to use and develop scientific knowledge and understanding	—	Pupils should investigate movement in a variety of devices, e.g. toys and models. They should be introduced to the idea of energy transfer.	4,4b
	4	Activities should help pupils to use and develop scientific knowledge and understanding	—	Pupils should have the opportunity to construct simple circuits	4,3a 4,4a
	5	Activities should help pupils to use and develop scientific knowledge and understanding	—	Pupils should have the opportunity to construct simple circuits	4,3a 4,4a
	6	Activities should help pupils to use and develop scientific knowledge and understanding	—	Pupils should investigate the formation of shadows and represent in drawings their ideas about how light varies in terms of brightness and shade	4,2d
Supplementary Units	7	Activities should encourage systematic listing and recording of data	1,3b 1,3c	—	—
	8	Actvities should encourage the raising and answering of questions	1,3a 1,3b 1,3c	Pupils should explore friction and investigate the ways in which the speed of an object can be changed	4,3c
	9	Activities should involve problems which can be solved qualitatively, but which increasingly allow for some quantification of variables	1,3a 1,3b	Pupils shouid explore different types of forces, including gravity	4,2c 4,3c

Toybox - Science in Action Key Stage 2 Book 1

National Curriculum Science — RECORD OF ACHIEVEMENT — NAME:

	Level 1	Level 2	Level 3	Level 4	Level 5
Attainment Target 1 **Science investigation**	a	a b c	a b c d	a b c	a b c
Attainment Target 2 **Life and Living processes**	a b	a b c d	a b c	a b c d	a b c d
Attainment Target 3 **Materials and their properties**	a	a b	a b c d e	a b c d e	a b c d
Attainment Target 4 **Physical processes**	a b c d	a b c d e	a b c d e	a b c d e	a b c d e f g

Science in Action Key Stage 2 Teacher's Guide